UltraPatterns

COLOR YOUR IMAGINATION WILD!

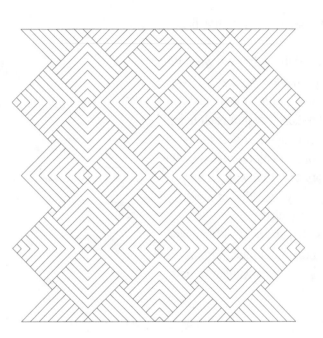

MindWare
FOR THE OTHER 90% OF YOUR BRAIN

MINDWARE
St. Paul, Minnesota

Explore the exquisite designs of hand-crafted quilts and textiles from far-away lands, and discover a fascinating world of symmetry and color variation. With each stroke of color, patterns begin coming to life—and with stunning results. You may even want to frame your favorites. *UltraPatterns* is a great way to "see the big picture." As individual thoughts link together patterns on paper, a wonderful thing happens. You begin to see patterns throughout every facet of life.

Each page is a fascinating image that is begging to be revealed. You'll find that every design is repeated, so you can color them different ways. What a wonderful avenue to unleashing that pent-up creativity swirling around that brain of yours!

So, let your imagination flow into each unique design. The high-quality paper is perfect for using felt-tip markers, crayons or colored pencils. Play with bold, bright colors or soften with creamy pastels. Let your ingenuity lead the way to producing your own masterpieces.

MindWare coloring books are ideal for classroom fun or endless hours of intrigue at home. Each book is so unique... it's just waiting to be explored by YOU.

Illustrations by Janice Porter

International Standard Book Number:
ISBN 1-892069-01-6

This book may be ordered from the publisher.

MindWare
2720 Patton Rd.
St. Paul, MN 55113
1-800-999-0398

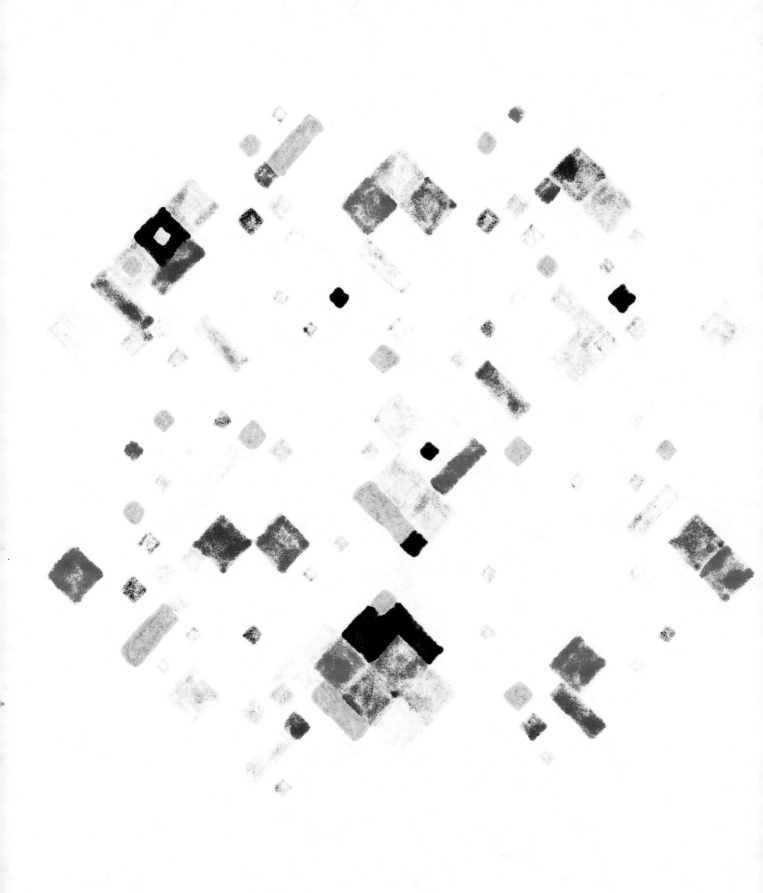

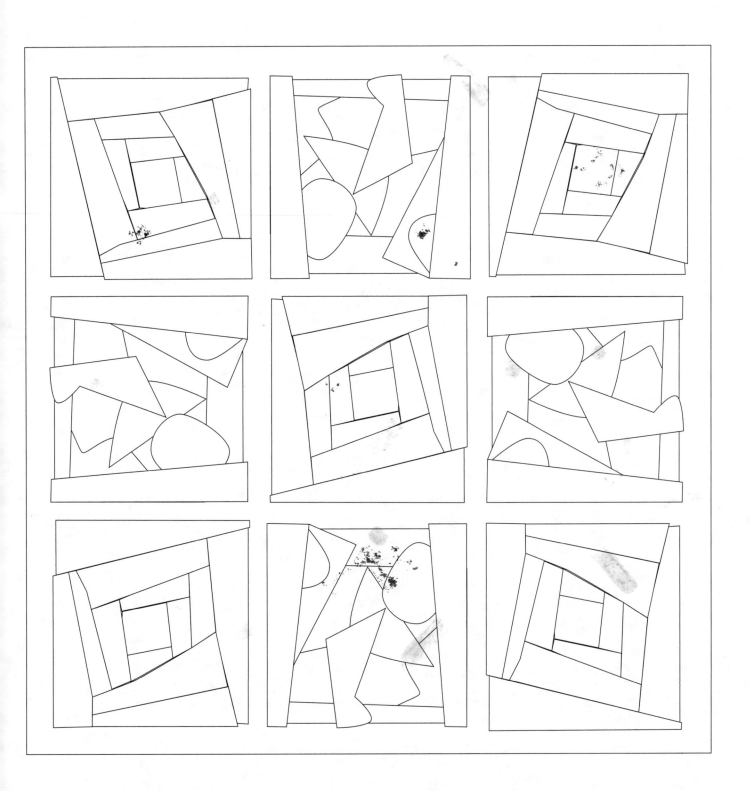

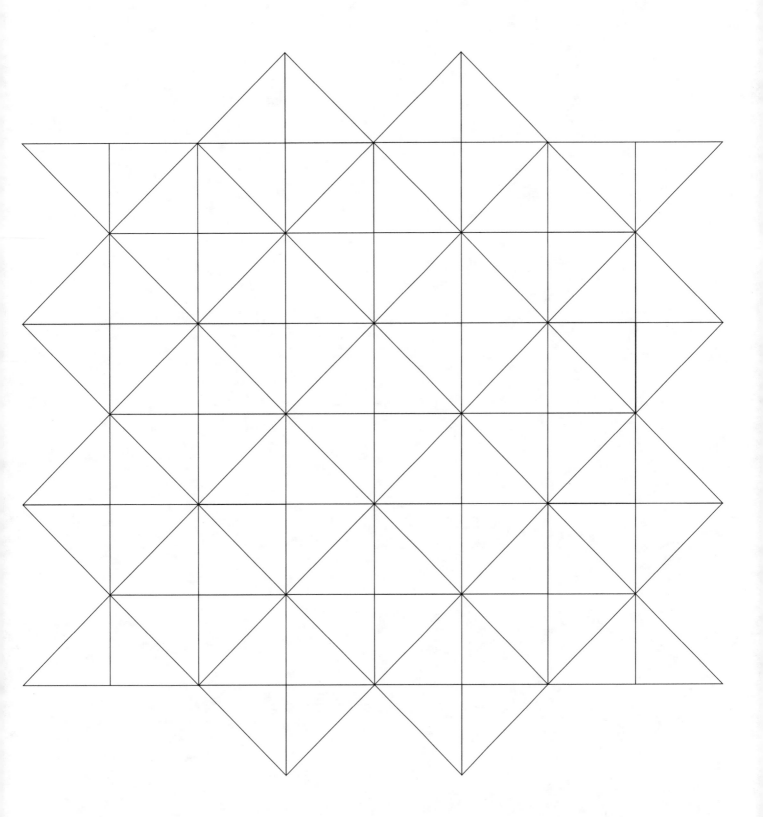

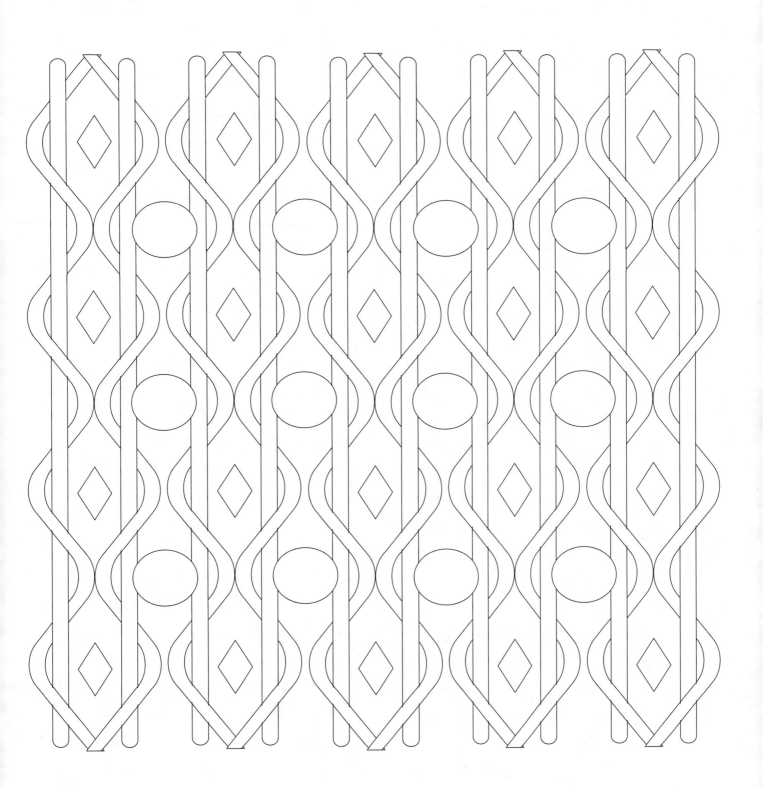

Kevin 2004

kevin Di 2014

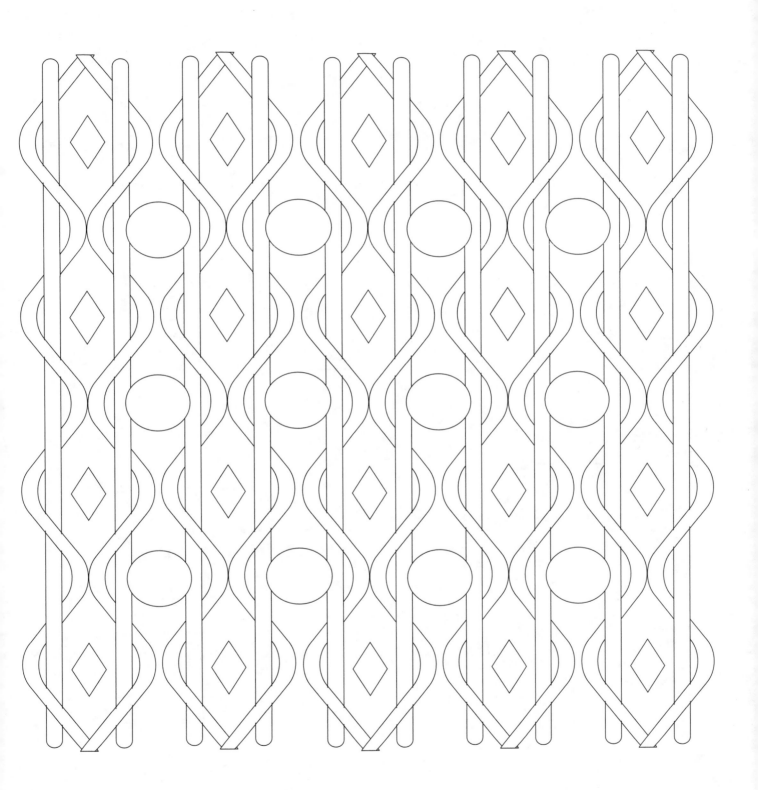